世界寓言画库

前 言

亲爱的读者：

　　今天，我们高兴地向你们献上一部珍贵的礼物——《世界寓言画库》，
这是《世界儿童文学名著大画库》的第二部，是一部中英文对照的大型连环
画集，希望你们喜欢。

　　寓言是一种隐含着讽喻意义的简短故事，它能为人们提供一些有益的
经验和教训，让人们懂得生活，少走弯路，少受挫折。它以短小的篇幅、深刻
的教训、生动活泼的故事、丰富具体的形象和精练明快的语言而博得了广大
小读者的喜爱，同时，也是家长们教育孩子的得力教材。

　　《世界寓言画库》精选了世界寓言368篇，其中中国寓言77篇，共
3300多幅图画，10个分册。

　　《世界寓言画库》的主编由全国著名的儿童文学家严文井先生担任，
由原全国连环画艺术研究会会长姜维朴先生担任艺术顾问。

　　《世界寓言画库》采用中、英两种文字，为学习英语的读者提供了良好
的阅读材料。为保证英文的规范性和准确性，我们聘请了美国俄亥俄州的
鲍伦格林州立大学的伊丽莎白女士担任英文总审核，对她的辛劳工作，我们
深表谢意。

编　者

2011 年 11 月

PREFACE

Dear friends,

Today, we present to you with pleasure a precious gift, *The Picture Treasury of World Fables*. The set of books is the second in the series The Great Picture Treasury of World Literary Masterpieces for Children. We hope you like it.

A fable is a short story meant to teach a moral lesson. It can let people know how to live and avoid detours and setbacks. It has a favourable reception among little friends for its short length, profound lessons, lively stories, varied and specific figures and succinct language; and what is more, it is also a helpful teaching material offered to parents.

The set selects three hundred and sixty-eight world fables including seventy-seven fables by Chinese writers, and consists of more than 3,300 pictures. It is collected in ten volumes.

The editor in chief of this set is Mr. Yan Wenjing, the famous Chinese writer of children's literature and the art advisor is Mr. Jiang Weipu, former president of the Chinese Institute of Picture-story Books.

The set is written both in Chinese and English. It serves as a good reading material for English learners. To ensure the accuracy and standardization of the translation in the set, we have invited Miss Elizabeth Wilson from Bowling Green State University, Ohio State of the United states to be the general editor of the translations. For her hard work, we express our deepest gratitude.

The Editors
November, 2011

目录
CONTENTS

野山羊和牧人 /1

狐狸和山羊 /5

狐狸和葡萄 /10

断尾狐 /13

肚胀的狐狸 /16

烧炭人和漂布人 /19

农夫和狼 /22

天文学家 /25

青蛙要国王 /28

北风和太阳 /33

农夫和狗 /37

老太婆和医生 /40

行人和熊 /44

发现金狮子的胆小鬼 /47

养蜂人 /50

鹿与狮子 /54

猫和老鼠 /59

猴子和骆驼 /63

生金蛋的鸡 /66

驴子与小狗 /69

母亲和她的女儿们 /73

宙斯和乌龟 /78

蚂蚁和蝉 /85

弹唱人 /90

小偷和公鸡 /95

狗和厨师 /100

衔肉的狗 /107

上当的狼 /112

狮子和农夫 /117

机警的公牛 /122

狮子和熊 /127

猩子和老鼠 /133

强盗和桑树 /139

狼和绵羊 /145

卖卜者 /151

年轻的浪子和燕子 /155

蝙蝠和黄鼠狼 /159

行人和阔叶树 /165

行人和蝮蛇 /169

驮神像的驴 /172

野驴 /175

驴、狐狸和狮子 /178

小偷和他的母亲 /182

The Wild Goat and the Goatherd /1

The Fox and the Goat /5

The Fox and Grapes /10

The Tailless Fox /13

A Bloated Fox /16

The Charcoal-burner and the Fuller /19

The Farmer and the Wolf /22

The Astronomer /25

The Frogs Who Asked For a King /28

The North Wind and the Sun /33

The Farmer and the Dogs /37

The Ole Woman and the Physician /40

The Travellers and the Bear /44

The Coward Who Found a Golden Lion /47

The Bee-man /50

The Deer and the Lion /54

The Cat and the Rats /59

The Monkey and the Camel /63

The Hen Laying Golden Eggs /66

The Donkey and the Lap-dog /69

The Mother and Her Daughters /73

Zeus and the Tortoise /78

The Ant and the Cicada /85

The Minstrel /90

The Thief and the Cock /95

The Dog and the Cook /100

A Dog with a Bit of Meat /107

The Dog Being Cheated /112

The Lion and the Farmer /117

The Wise Bull /122

The Lion and the Bear /127

The Lion and the Mouse /133

The Robber and the Mulberry Tree /139

The Wolf and the Sheep /145

The Fortune-teller /151

The Young Loafer and the Swallow /155

The Bat and the Weasel /159

Pedestrians and the Broadleaf Tree /165

The Pedestrian and the Pallas Pit Viper /169

The Donkey Carrying a God Statue /172

The Wild Ass /175

The Ass, the Fox and the Lion /178

The Thief and His Mother /182

野山羊和牧人

THE WILD GOAT AND THE GOATHERD

原著:〔古希腊〕伊索   Written by Aesop(Gr.)

改编:春 雨   Adapted by Chun Yu

翻译:李小飞   Translated by Li Xiaofei

绘画:姜文浩   Illustrated by Jiang Wenhao

(1)一个牧人发现一只野山羊同自己的羊混在一起。

A goatherd found a wild goat mingle among his goats.

（2）傍晚，牧人便把野山羊同自己的羊一起赶进了羊圈。

In the evening, he drove the wild goat and his own into the fold.

（3）第二天,起了风暴。他便把羊留在圈里喂养。

Next day, it stormed. The goatherd kept the wild goat in the fold and fed it.

（4）他一心想把野山
羊变成自己的羊，便
特意给它多加饲料。

In the hope of
making it his own, he
fed it more food.

（5）风暴停息了，羊
群来到草地上。不
料，野山羊却逃跑
了。

When the storm
stopped, the flock
came to the grass-
land; but unexpect-
edly the wild goat ran
away.

（6）牧人追上野山羊，责怪它忘恩负义。

The goatherd caught up with him and blamed his ungracious behavior.

（7）山羊说："我看你对我比对你的羊还要好，我担心上当。"

The wild goat said,"I saw that you treated me better than your own goats, so I'm cautious of being fooled."

狐狸和山羊

THE FOX AND THE GOAT

原著:〔古希腊〕伊索　　　Written by Aesop(Gr.)

改编:春　雨　　　　　　Adapted by Chun Yu

翻译:李小飞　　　　　　Translated by Li Xiaofei

绘画:梁平波　　　　　　Illustrated by Liang Pingbo

(1)一只狐狸落在井里,上不来,干着急没办法。

A fox fell into a well and could not get out. He was anxious but unable to do anything.

（2）一只干渴的山羊来到井边,看见狐狸,问道:"井水好喝吗? "

A thirsty goat came to the well, saw the fox and asked, "Is that water good?"

（3）狐狸忙说:"这水甜极了,快下来喝吧!"

The fox replied promptly, "It is the sweetest. Come down and try it. "

（4）山羊听了，想也没想，就跳了下去。

　　With this, the goat jumped down without thinking.

（5）山羊和狐狸同样陷入了困境。狐狸心生一计。

　　The goat, like the fox, fell into a difficult position. Meanwhile, the fox had an idea in mind.

（6）它对山羊说："我踩着你先跳上去，再拉你出去。"

He said to the goat,"I climb up your back and get out first, and then I can drag you out. "

（7）山羊同意了。狐狸踩着羊背爬出了井口。

The goat agreed. So the fox stepped on the goat's back and climbed out.

（8）狐狸上去后，扭头要走。山羊生气地责备它背信弃义。

After he was out, the fox turned away and started to go on his way. The goat blamed the fox angrily for his betrayal.

（9）狐狸说："傻瓜，你若稍有头脑，就不会盲目地跳下去了。"

The fox said, "You fool, if you had a little brain, you wouldn't jump down blindly."

狐狸和葡萄

THE FOX AND GRAPES

原著:〔古希腊〕伊索　　　Written by Aesop (Gr.)

改编:春　雨　　　　　　Adapted by Chun Yu

翻译:李小飞　　　　　　Translated by Li Xiaofei

绘画:梁平波　　　　　　Illustrated by Liang Pingbo

（1）一只饥饿的狐狸在到处觅食。它转来转去,什么也没找到。

A hungry fox was looking for food everywhere,He moved round but found nothing.

（2）忽然,它看见一棵葡萄树,树上长着一串串晶莹欲滴的葡萄。

Suddenly, he spied a vine with clusters of crystal-clear and juicy grapes.

（3）葡萄散发着又甜又香的气味,馋得狐狸垂涎三尺。

The grapes sent forth so sweet and so fragrant a smell that the fox's mouth drooled with greed.

（4）它蹦跳着去摘葡萄，可总也摸不着，急得它团团转。

He jumped to reach the grapes, but did not succeed. So he moved round and round anxiously.

（5）最后，狐狸说："这葡萄一定是酸的!"灰心丧气地离去了。

At last, the fox said, "These grapes are surely sour." So he walked off disappointedly.

断尾狐

THE TAILLESS FOX

原著：〔古希腊〕伊索　　　Written by Aesop (Gr.)

改编：春　雨　　　　　　Adapted by Chun Yu

翻译：孙　健　　　　　　Translated by Sun Jian

绘画：孙爱国 孙丹青　　　Illustrated by Sun Aiguo and Sun Danqing

（1）有只狐狸被捕兽器夹断了尾巴。

One fox had its tail cut accidentally by a beast-catcher.

（2）它认为这是奇耻大辱，难过得整日愁眉苦脸。

It thought that was a great shame and had a worried look on his face all the day.

（3）它决定劝所有的狐狸都去掉尾巴，以掩饰自己的缺点。

It decided to advise all the other foxes to cut their tails away in order to cover the shortcoming of itself.

（4）它对伙伴们说:"有条尾巴太不雅观了,去掉吧!"

"It's not so nice to have a tail. It should be cut away,"it said to its partners.

（5）一只狐狸一针见血地说:"你若有尾巴,就不会劝我们割掉了。"

One fox pointed out sharply:"If you had your tail,you would never advise us to cut ours off."

肚胀的狐狸

A BLOATED FOX

原著：〔古希腊〕伊索　　　　Written by Aesop（Gr.）

改编：春　雨　　　　　　　　Adapted by Chun Yu

翻译：王宁娜　　　　　　　　Translated by Wang Ningna

绘画：杜云河　　　　　　　　Illustrated by Du Yunhe

（1）一只饥饿的狐狸，到处找食吃。

A hungry fox was looking for something to eat everywhere.

（2）忽然，它发现了树洞里牧人放的面包，便钻进去一顿猛吃。

Suddenly, he found some bread saved by a shepherd in a tree-hole. He got into the hole and swallowed the bread greedily.

（3）不料，肚子暴胀，从树洞里钻不出来了。狐狸叫苦连天。

Unexpectedly, his belly was so bloated after overeating that he couldn't get himself out of the tree hole. The fox grumbled incessantly.

（4）一只过路的狐
狸听见了,跑过去问
发生了什么事。

A passing-by
fox heard the cry and
went to ask what had
happened.

（5）它听后说道:
"你不再偷吃别人
的东西时就能出来
了。"

When he knew
it, he said:"You
won't get out until
you stop stealing
other's food."

烧炭人和漂布人

THE CHARCOAL-BURNER
AND THE FULLER

原著:〔古希腊〕伊索

改编:春 雨

翻译:李小飞

绘画:董小明

Written by Aesop (Gr.)

Adapted by Chun Yu

Translated by Li Xiaofei

Illustrated by Dong Xiaoming

（1）一个烧炭人租了一所房子,在里面营业。

A charcoal-burner rented a house and carried on his trade there.

（2）一天，他看见一个漂布人走来，就热情地邀请他一块住。

One day, he saw a fuller walking by and entreated the fuller to live with him.

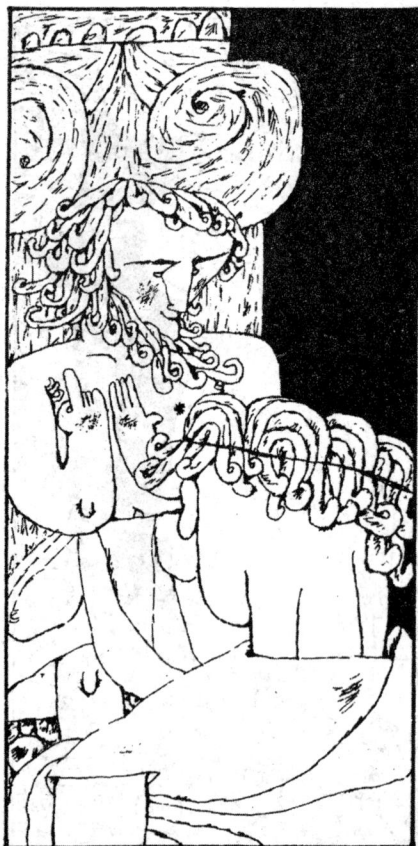

（3）烧炭人说："这样我们可以互相帮助，再说，住在一块也省钱。"

The charcoal-burner said, "In this way, we can help each other and what's more, lessen our expenses."

（4）漂布人断然拒绝道："这是绝对不行的。""为什么？"烧炭人问。

The fuller refused to do so and said,"It is absolutely impossible.""Why?"asked the charcoal-burner.

（5）漂布人说："因为我是漂白布的，而你是烧黑炭的，黑白混淆不得。"

The fuller said,"Because I'm whitening cloth while you're burning charcoal. White and black should not be mixed up."

农夫和狼

THE FARMER AND THE WOLF

原著:〔古希腊〕伊索　　Written by Aesop（Gr.）

改编: 春　雨　　　　　Adapted by Chun Yu

翻译: 李小飞　　　　　Translated by Li Xiaofei

绘画: 周　申　　　　　Illustrated by Zhou Shen

（1）农夫解下拉犁的牛,牵去饮水。

A farmer untied the bull which was pulling a plough and led it to drink water.

（2）有只饥饿的狼出
来觅食，看见犁，走
过去舔起牛套来。

A hungry wolf,
out to seek food, saw
the plough and went
up to lick it.

（3）它不知不觉地把
脖子伸进了牛套中却
退不出来了。

He stretched his
neck into the yoke
without his knowing
it and then could not
get out.

（4）狼恼火地拖着犁在田地上转来转去。

The wolf angrily dragged the plough from side to side in the field.

（5）农夫看见了，说道："坏家伙，但愿你真的能改邪归正。"

On seeing that, the farmer said, "Scoundrel, let's see you can give up evil and return to good."

天文学家

THE ASTRONOMER

原著:〔古希腊〕伊索

改编: 春 雨

翻译: 李小飞

绘画: 袁 晖

Written by Aesop (Gr.)

Adapted by Chun Yu

Translated by Li Xiaofei

Illustrated by Yuan Hui

（1）有个天文学家,每天晚上都到外面去观测星象。

An astronomer used to walk out every night to observe stars.

（2）有一天，他按时到城外去观星象。

One evening, he went to the suburbs to observe stars in time.

（3）因为他一边走一边望着天空，一不留神落在一口井里。

Because he gazed at the sky while walking, he fell, unawares, into a well.

（4）他大声呼叫起来，一个过路人听见了，走过来，把他拖了上来。

He cried loudly for help. A passerby heard his cries, came and pulled him up.

（5）过路人说："朋友，你怎么只观察天上的情况，却不看地上的事情呢！"

He said to the astronomer, "Friend, while you are trying to observe what's in the sky, why don't you overlook what is on earth?"

青蛙要国王

THE FROGS WHO ASKED
FOR A KING

原著:〔古希腊〕伊索　　　Written by Aesop (Gr.)

改编:春　雨　　　　　　Adapted by Chun Yu

翻译:李小飞　　　　　　Translated by Li Xiaofei

绘画:李　光　　　　　　Illustrated by Li Guang

（1）青蛙没有首领，觉得不痛快。

The frogs were not happy because they did not have a ruler.

（2）它们派代表去见宙斯，要求给它们派一个国王。

So they sent to Zeus to ask him to give them a king.

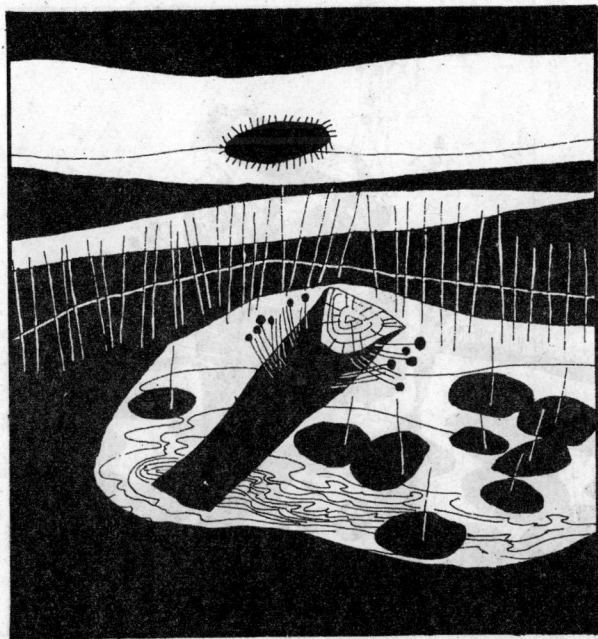

（3）宙斯看它们太天真，就把一块木头扔到池塘里。

Zeus thought that they were too naive, and then into the pond he threw a big log.

（4）青蛙听见扑通
一声，吓得全都钻进
池塘水下去了。

The frogs heard
a splash and were
frightened into hid-
ing deep in the pond.

（5）后来，它们见木
头国王没什么了不
起，就爬到上边去
玩。

By and by, they
looked at the log.
The king was noth-
ing. So they hopped
upon it and amused
themselves.

（6）它们觉得这个国王太迟钝，很不满意。

They felt this king was too stupid and were not satisfied with it.

（7）它们又去见宙斯，要求换一个国王。

Again they sent to Zeus and begged him to give them another king.

（8）宙斯生了气,给
它们派去一条水蛇。

　　Zeus got angry
and sent them a wa-
ter snake.

（9）水蛇抓住青蛙
就吃。青蛙们好后
悔。

　　The snake
caught frogs and
swallowed them.
How regretful the
frogs were!

北风和太阳

THE NORTH WIND AND THE SUN

原著:〔古希腊〕伊索   Written by Aesop (Gr.)

改编:春 雨   Adapted by Chun Yu

翻译:李小飞   Translated by Li Xiaofei

绘画:黄勤勤   Illustrated by Huang Qinqin

(1)北风和太阳争论谁的威力大。

The north wind and the sun disputed who was more powerful.

（2）它们议定:谁能剥去行人的衣裳,谁就算胜利。

They agreed: whoever could disrobe a traveller would win.

（3）北风猛刮起来,行人把衣裳裹紧,北风就刮得更猛。

The north wind began to blow hard, but the traveller wrapped his clothes around him, so it blew a most furious blast.

（4）行人冷得厉害，
便又加上了更多的
衣裳。

The traveller felt
so cold that he put on
more clothes.

（5）北风终于刮累
了，精疲力尽地退了
下来。

The north wind
was eventually wea-
ried and withdrew.

（6）太阳出来了。它暖暖地晒着，行人脱掉了棉衣。

Then came the sun, sending his warm rays. The traveller took off his cotton-padded jacket.

（7）它越晒越猛，行人热得难受，只得脱光衣服，下河洗澡。

He shone out with more and more warmth. The traveller could hardly overcome with the heat, undressed and bathed in the river.

农夫和狗

THE FARMER AND THE DOGS

原著：〔古希腊〕伊索　　　　Written by Aesop (Gr.)

改编：春 雨　　　　　　　　Adapted by Chun Yu

翻译：王 萍 谊 鸣　　　　　Translated by Wang Ping and Yi Ming

绘画：张卫东　　　　　　　　Illustrated by Zhang Weidong

（1）农夫被风暴困在家里，断了食物，只好把绵羊宰了吃。

A farmer was detained by a storm in his house. He ran out of food. So in order to eat he had to kill his sheep.

（2）暴风还是刮个不停，他又把山羊吃了。

The storm continued hard. He had to kill his goat.

（3）暴风仍然没有减弱，他又把耕牛宰了。

The storm still continued. His yoke ox was killed for food again.

（4）他养的几条狗见此情景，非常害怕。

On seeing this, his dogs feared very much.

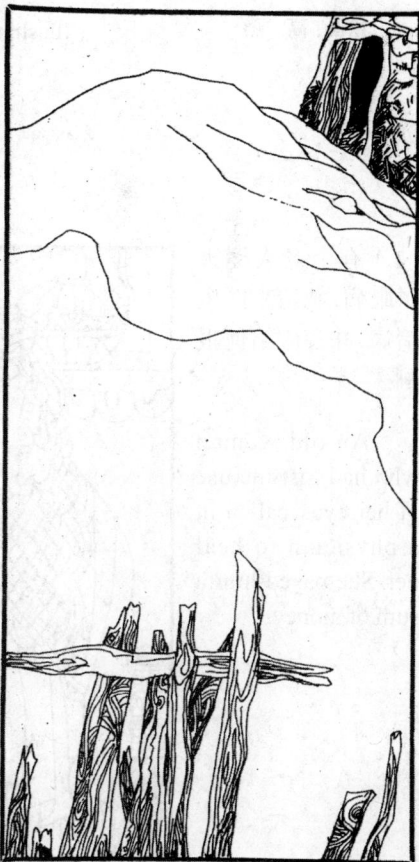

（5）它们商议说："快逃走吧！主人连牛都宰了，何况我们？"当夜就溜了。

They took counsel together and said:"It is time for us to escape. Even the ox has been killed. How can we expect him to spare us?"They ran away that night.

老太婆和医生

THE OLD WOMAN AND THE PHYSICIAN

原著:〔古希腊〕伊索   Written by Aesop (Gr.)

改编: 春 雨   Adapted by Chun Yu

翻译: 王 萍 谊 鸣   Translated by Wang Ping and Yi Ming

绘画: 高 燕   Illustrated by Gao Yan

（1）有个老太婆害了眼病,她请来医生治病,并答应给他报酬。

An old woman who had lost the use of her eyes, called in a physician to heal her. She payed him a sum of money.

（2）那医生每次来治病时，都趁机偷走她家一件东西。

On each visit the physician took something away with him.

（3）老太婆家的东西全被偷光了，她的眼病也治好了。

When the old woman's eyes were fully recovered from her illness, all property had been stolen by the physician.

（4）最后，医生向老太婆索取报酬，老太婆不肯给。

The physician demanded the promised payment at last, but the old woman refused to give it to him.

（5）两人拉拉扯扯地去打官司。

They dragged each other to the court.

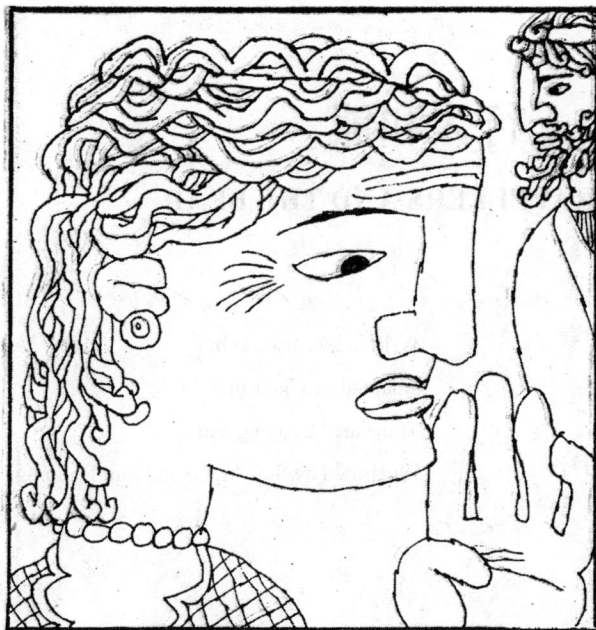

（6）老太婆说："讲定治好眼我才给报酬，可我的眼反倒坏了。"

The old woman said, "I promised to give him a sum of money only if I should recover my sight. But on the contrary, my eyes are even worse."

（7）"以前，家里的东西我都能看见，如今我什么也看不见了。"

"I could see in my house various goods before. But now, I can't see a single thing in it."

行人和熊

THE TRAVELLERS AND THE BEAR

原著:〔古希腊〕伊索
改编:陈 进
翻译:江 韵
绘画:孙爱国 孙丹青

Written by Aesop (Gr.)
Adapted by Chen Jin
Translated by Jiang Yun
Illustrated by Sun Aiguo and Sun Danqing

（1）有一对好朋友，一高一矮。一天，他们在林中赶路,遇见了一只熊。

There were two good friends. One was tall and the other was short. While they were walking in the forest, they came across a bear.

（2）高个子只顾自
己,爬上树,藏了起
来。小个子无处躲
藏,只好趴在地上装
死。

Caring only for
his own safety, the
tall man climbed up
a tree and hid him-
self. The short man
had no place to hide,
and had to lie on the
ground, pretending to
be dead.

（3）熊来到小个子
跟前,在他脸上嗅了
嗅,调头走开了。原
来熊不吃死人。

The bear came
up and smelled the
short man on the
face. Then it turned
its head and walked
away. Actually, bears
did not eat dead
men.

（4）高个子从树上溜下来，奇怪地问小个子："熊在你耳边说的什么？"

The tall man slid down the tree, and asked the short man curiously,"What has the bear said to you?"

（5）小个子回答："熊说，以后千万不要和那种不能共患难的朋友同行。"

The short man answered,"The bear said,'Never travel with a friend who can't go through thick and thin together later.'"

发现金狮子的胆小鬼

THE COWARD WHO FOUND A
GOLDEN LION

原著：〔古希腊〕伊索　　　　　Written by Aesop (Gr.)

改编：陈　进　　　　　　　　　Adapted by Chen Jin

翻译：王　萍　王明波　　　　　Translated by Wang Ping and Wang Mingbo

绘画：孙爱国　孙丹青　　　　　Illustrated by Sun Aiguo and Sun Danqing

（1）有个胆小而贪财的人发现了一只金狮子。

There was a timid and greedy man who found a golden lion.

（2）他又惊又喜,不知是祸是福,躲得远远地观望着。

Filled with joy and surprise, he didn't know whether it was a disaster or a happiness. So he hid himself far away and kept looking at it.

（3）他渴望得到金子,但却怕狮子伤害自己,急得他抓耳搔腮。

He thirsted for the gold, but was afraid of being hurt by the lion. He became very irritable.

（4）他转来转去, 左
右为难: 该怎么办
呢?

　　He went here
and there in a dilem-
ma. What to do then?

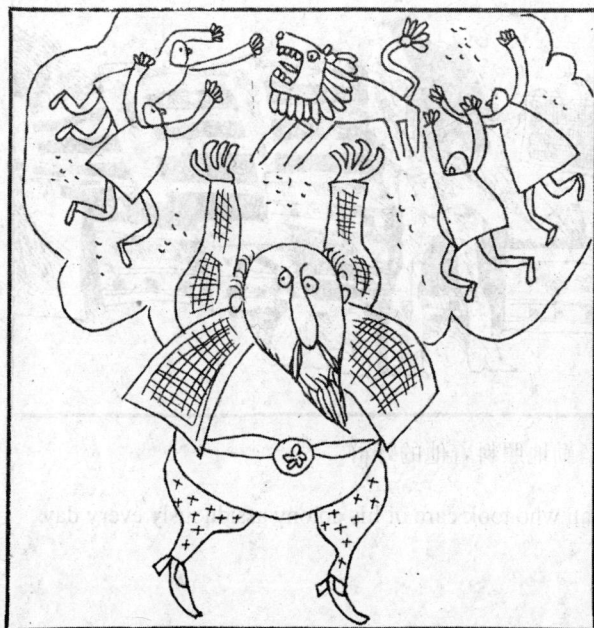

（5）他终于想出了一
个两全其美的办法:
让家里的人来捉拿,
他躲在远处观看。

　　He came up with
a good idea at last: let
his family members
catch it, and he just
hid himself far away
to have a look.

养蜂人

THE BEE-MAN

原著:〔古希腊〕伊索 Written by Aesop (Gr.)

改编: 陈 进 Adapted by Chen Jin

翻译: 王 萍 王明波 Translated by Wang Ping and Wang Mingbo

绘画: 李承东 Illustrated by Li Chengdong

（1）有个养蜂人，每天辛勤地照料着他的蜂群。

There was a bee-man who took care of his colony assiduously every day.

（2）一天，小偷溜进养蜂人的家里，趁主人不在，把蜜和蜂巢偷走了。

One day when the bee-man was out, a thief stole into the beehive and took off with the bees' honeycomb.

（3）养蜂人回来，见蜂箱空了，着急地四处寻找。

When the bee-man came back, he found the beehive was empty. He was very anxious, and looked for it everywhere.

（4）这时，蜜蜂们采花归来，不见了蜂巢，气得嗡嗡乱叫。

At this time, the bees returned after picking flowers. When they found their beehive had disappeared, they buzzed angrily.

（5）它们看见了养蜂人，蜂拥而上，凶狠地蜇起他来。

Seeing the bee-man, they went into action simultaneously, stinging him fiercely and maliciously.

（6）养蜂人一边躲闪一边指责："你们太无知了,怎么冲我来了?"

The bee-man did thin stings. Blaming them, he screamed, "You are too ignorant! Why should you strike me?"

（7）蜜蜂们恍然大悟,不该放过敌人,而攻击关心自己的人。

The bees suddenly realized that they shouldn't let the enemy get away, and attack the person who took good care of them.

鹿与狮子

THE DEER AND THE LION

原著:〔古希腊〕伊索　　　Written by Aesop (Gr.)

改编:歌　风　　　　　　Adapted by Ge Feng

翻译:孙　健　　　　　　Translated by Sun Jian

绘画:赵勤国　　　　　　Illustrated by Zhao Qinguo

（1）一只鹿口渴了,它看见前面有一潭清清的泉水,高兴地跑了过去。

Once upon a time there was a deer who felt very thirsty.He saw a pool of clear spring water and ran to it cheerfully.

（2）鹿角映在水里，英俊挺拔，鹿非常得意。

He saw his handsome deerhorns mirrored in the water and felt very satisfied and proud.

（3）但是，当鹿看见自己又细又弱的脚的倒影时，不禁厌恶起来。

But when he saw his thin and weak feet in the water, he started to hate them.

（4）这时候，远处出现了一头狮子，朝鹿追来。

Just then, a lion appeared far from the distance and ran towards him.

（5）鹿大吃一惊，撒腿就跑。它的腿矫捷灵活，疾如飞箭，狮子也追不上它。

The deer was frightened and started to run. His legs were brisk and quick, and carried him as fast as an arrow. The lion failed to catch him.

（6）鹿很轻松地逃脱狮子的追赶,躲在树林中,又摇头摆尾地欣赏起自己美丽的角来。

The deer easily escaped from the lion. Then he hid himself in a forest and started enjoying his own deerhorns again.

（7）不料,狮子寻踪追来了,鹿转身又逃。树枝密布,鹿角磕磕绊绊。

To his surprise, the lion suddenly arrived after following the traces. The deer turned back to escape. But his deer-horns knocked against too many branches of trees.

（8）突然，鹿角被树枝挂住了。狮子扑上来，把鹿咬住了。

Suddenly the deerhorns were blocked by branches of trees. The lion sprang to the deer and gripped him with his teeth.

（9）鹿临死叹道："我所讨厌的脚救了我，而我喜欢的角却害了我，我好糊涂啊!"

The deer lamented before dying:"How silly I am! It's the feet I hated which saved me, but it's the horns I loved which killed me."

猫和老鼠

THE CAT AND THE RATS

原著：〔古希腊〕伊索   Written by Aesop (Gr.)

改编：歌 风   Adapted by Ge Feng

翻译：孙 健   Translated by Sun Jian

绘画：姜昌宁   Illustrated by Jiang Changning

（1）在一户人家，有许多老鼠，它们非常猖狂，闹得主人不得安宁。

In one household there were many rats. They were very savage and made the house-owner quite worried.

（2）一只猫知道后，
跑来和老鼠交朋友，
悄悄地把几只老鼠
吃掉。

Hearing that,
one cat came and
made friends with
the rats. He ate sev-
eral rats quietly.

（3）老鼠发觉伙伴
在减少，躲进洞里不
敢出来。

Finding the
partners were reduc-
ing, the other rats hid
themselves in their
carven and didn't
dare to go out.

（4）猫吃不到老鼠，馋得团团转：唉，怎么把老鼠引出来呢？

The cat couldn't eat rats any more. It walked round and round because of greediness. It thought, "How can I lure the rats out of the cavern?"

（5）猫爬到窗台上，倒挂下来，装作死了的样子。

The cat climbed onto the windowsill and hung himself face down, pretending to be dead.

（6）一只老鼠溜到洞口窥探，说："哼，你就是变成一只皮袋，我们也不会上当了。"

One rat stole to the hole of its cavern to spy upon the cat and said: "Humph!I'll never be taken in even if you can change yourself into a sack."

（7）猫见老鼠不再上当，只好饿着肚皮悻悻地走了。

Because the rats couldn't be tricked any more, the cat had to leave with hunger angrily.

猴子和骆驼

THE MONKEY AND THE CAMEL

原著:〔古希腊〕伊索　　　Written by Aesop (Gr.)

改编:陈　进　　　　　　Adapted by Chen Jin

翻译:王　萍　王明波　　Translated by Wang Ping and Wang Mingbo

绘画:蒲慧华　　　　　　Illustrated by Pu Huihua

（1）新年到了,兽类集会欢度新年。

The new year was coming. The beasts gathered together to celebrate it.

（2）小猴子跳起了
欢快的舞蹈，赢得了
大家的一致称赞。

A little monkey
danced cheerfully,
winning praise from
all.

（3）骆驼非常忌妒
小猴子，它也想获得
同样的荣誉。

The camel en-
vied the little mon-
key very much. He
wanted to win the
same honour.

（4）于是，它走上舞台跳了起来，动作笨拙，尽出怪相。

So he came onto the stage, and danced. His action was clumsy and odd.

（5）伙伴们很生气，异口同声地把它轰了下去。

Being very angry, the companions hooted him off the stage with one voice.

生金蛋的鸡

THE HEN LAYING GOLDEN EGGS

原著:〔古希腊〕伊索

改编: 歌 风

翻译: 王 萍 谊 鸣

绘画: 蒲慧华

Written by Aesop (Gr.)

Adapted by Ge Feng

Translated by Wang Ping and Yi Ming

Illustrated by Pu Huihua

(1) 有个人养了一只母鸡,他想从鸡身上得到好处。

A man had a hen and he wanted to get some benefits from it.

（2）一天，母鸡下了一个蛋，竟是纯金的。

One day, the hen laid him an egg. It was a pure golden egg.

（3）这人喜出望外，他以为鸡肚子里一定全是金块，便把鸡杀了。

The man was pleasantly surprised. He supposed the hen must contain many golden pieces, therefore he killed it.

（4）不料，剖开肚子一看，跟普通的母鸡一模一样。

To his surprise, when he cut it open, he found the hen differed in no respect from any other hens.

（5）这人好后悔！为了得到大笔财富，结果断了财源。

How regretful he was! In order to get more treasures, however, he deprived himself of financial resources.

驴子与小狗

THE DONKEY AND THE LAP-DOG

原著：〔古希腊〕伊索　　Written by Aesop（Gr.）

改编：歌　风　　　　　Adapted by Ge Feng

翻译：王　萍　谊　鸣　　Translated by Wang Ping and Yi Ming

绘画：孙爱国　孙丹青　　Illustrated by Sun Aiguo and Sun Danqing

（1）有个人，养了一只玛耳太狗和一头驴子。

A man owned a Maltese dog and a donkey.

（2）驴子常常和小
狗在一起做游戏，相
处得非常和睦。

The donkey
often played games
with the dog and they
lived together amica-
bly.

（3）一天，主人从外
边吃饭回来，带回一
块馅饼。

One day, their
master came back
after a dinner outside
and brought back a
cake.

（4）狗蹦蹦跳跳地迎上去向主人摇尾巴。主人很高兴，撕下一块馅饼扔给了它。

Frisking and jumping, the dog walked toward his master wagging his tail. The master was very glad and gave him a piece of cake.

（5）驴子好羡慕，也蹦跳着跑到主人面前甩起尾巴，"啪!"主人脸上挨了一下。

With admiration, the donkey ran to his master and wagged his tail in front of his master. "Bang!" The master's face was spanked.

（6）主人大为恼火，把驴子痛打了一顿。

The master was very angry and beat the donkey very hard.

（7）驴子被拴在木桩上。它不明白，主人怎么不能一视同仁呢？

The donkey was chained to a tree. It didn't know why its master couldn't treat it equally without discrimination.

母亲和她的女儿们

THE MOTHER AND HER DAUGHTERS

原著:〔古希腊〕伊索　　　　Written by Aesop (Gr.)

改编:陈 进　　　　　　　　Adapted by Chen Jin

翻译:孙 健　　　　　　　　Translated by Sun Jian

绘画:高 燕　　　　　　　　Illustrated by Gao Yan

（1）一个妇人有两个女儿,她非常疼爱她们。

An old lady had two daughters and loved them very dearly.

（2）大女儿嫁给了
一个种菜的农民。

The elder
daughter married a
vegetable grower.

（3）小女儿嫁给了
一个烧砖的窑工。

The younger
daughter married a
brickkiln worker.

（4）一天，母亲到大女儿家去，想看看女儿生活得怎么样。

One day, the mother went to the home of the elder daughter to see how she was.

（5）大女儿说："妈妈，天旱无雨，菜田都干坏了，请您为我们求雨吧！"

The elder daughter said: "Mum. There's no rain now and the vegetable fields are too dry. Please pray for us to have rain."

（6）第二天，母亲又来到小女儿家。小两口热情地迎接她。

The following day, the mother went to the home of the younger daughter. The young couple entertained her warmly.

（7）小女儿说：“妈妈，为了让坯干得快些，请您为我们祈求苍天，让阳光更猛烈些吧!”

The younger daughter said: "Mum, please pray for us for stronger sunshine to make the unfired bricks dry faster."

（8）母亲为难地说：
"你望天晴，你姐姐
却盼下雨呢！"

The mother said embarrassedly: "You're expecting sunny days, but your sister is expecting rain."

（9）慈祥的母亲左右为难：我究竟该为哪一个女儿祈求呢？

The kind mother felt embarrassed this time: "For which daughter should I pray?"

宙斯和乌龟

ZEUS AND THE TORTOISE

原著:〔古希腊〕伊索　　　Written by Aesop (Gr.)

改编: 芊　里　　　　　　 Adapted by Qian Li

翻译: 王　萍　王明波　　 Translated by Wang Ping and Wang Mingbo

绘画: 梁平波　　　　　　 Illustrated by Liang Pingbo

（1）宙斯结婚,举办了盛大的婚礼。

　　Zeus got married. He had a grand wedding.

（2）动物们都来了，还带来了精彩的节目。

All the animals came and brought wonderful programmes.

（3）瞧，犀牛的角斗，惊心动魄。

Look, the fight between rhinoceros was soul-stirring.

（4）听，狮子的合唱，震动山河。

Listen, the chorus of the lions shook the valley and river.

（5）鸵鸟的舞姿矫健豪迈。

The dance movement of the ostrich was vigorous and generous.

（6）孔雀的开屏舞婀娜多姿。

The peacocks spread its tail and danced gracefully.

（7）企鹅的群舞富有爵士风度。

The penguin's mass dance had the poise of gentlemen.

（8）动物们载歌载舞，宙斯乐不可支。

The animals were dancing and singing. Zeus was overjoyed.

（9）忽然，宙斯发现乌龟没有到场，心中顿生不快。

Suddenly Zeus found the tortoise was not present. So he felt unhappy at once.

（10）他命令小鹿去找乌龟，问它为什么缺席。

He ordered the fawn to look for the tortoise and ask why it was absent.

（11）乌龟对小鹿说：“家多么可爱，我不愿离开。”

The tortoise told the fawn:"How lovely home is. I don't want to leave it. "

（12）宙斯很生气，罚乌龟永远驮着自己的家。

Zeus was very angry, and then punished the tortoise by making it carry its home on its back forever.

（13）从此，乌龟的房子就长在了背上，走到哪儿就带到哪儿。

Hence, the home of the tortoise grew on its back, and it carried it wherever it went.

蚂蚁和蝉

THE ANT AND THE CICADA

原著:〔古希腊〕伊索	Written by Aesop (Gr.)
改编:芊 里	Adapted by Qian Li
翻译:王 萍 谊 鸣	Translated by Wang Ping and Yi Ming
绘画:袁 晖	Illustrated by Yuan Hui

（1）夏天,蝉在树上扯着喉咙大喊大叫,好快活!

In summer, a cicada cried out on the tree in a high voice. How happy it was!

（2）蚂蚁却在忙忙碌碌地准备过冬的粮食。

Meanwhile, ants were collecting food for winter on the tree.

（3）蝉讥笑蚂蚁:"小傻瓜,光知道干活,瞧我多欢乐!"

The cicada inquired of the ant:"Blockhead, you just know working. Look at me, what a happy life!"

（4）蚂蚁不以为然地摇摇头，继续运粮食去了。

Showing disapproval of that, the ant shook its head and continued to transport food.

（5）冬天来到了，蚂蚁丰衣足食，一家安安乐乐。

Winter was coming; the ant had ample food and clothing. The whole family was comfortable and peaceful.

（6）蝉家无粒米，饿得瑟瑟发抖，只好四处乞讨。

The family of the cicada had not a single bit of food, and shivered with cold. It had to beg for food everywhere.

（7）蝉来到蚂蚁洞口，见它们正在翻晒受潮的粮食，便上前讨借。

The cicada came to the hole of ant and saw some ants were busy drying grain in the sun. He asked for food.

（8）蚂蚁眨了它一眼:"你只知道夏天唱歌快乐,可为什么不想想冬天怎么办?"

The ant glanced at the cicada and said:"You just know singing. Won't that do as well in winter?"

（9）蝉的脸一阵通红,说不出话来。

The cicada blushed with shame and said nothing.

弹唱人

THE MINSTREL

原著：〔古希腊〕伊索　　　Written by Aesop（Gr.）

改编：芊　里　　　　　　Adapted by Qian Li

翻译：王　萍　王明波　　Translated by Wang Ping and Wang Mingbo

绘画：黄勤勤　　　　　　Illustrated by Huang Qinqin

（1）有个愚蠢的弹唱人，梦想成为一名出色的歌手。

There was a stupid man who could play and sing. He dreamed of being an outstanding singer.

（2）可是,他的嗓子太差,像干裂的竹筒。

But he had a bad voice just like a dried-up bamboo tube.

（3）他在山坡上弹唱,动物纷纷逃避。

He sang and played on the hillside. The animals escaped one after another.

（4）他在树林中弹
唱，鸟儿便不得安
宁。

He sang and
played in the woods.
The birds had no
peace.

（5）他只好躲在家
中粉刷过的室内弹
唱。

He had to stay
in a room which was
just painted, singing
and playing.

（6）墙壁发出嗡嗡的回音,仿佛他的嗓音优美了。

There was a buzz echo on the wall. It seemed that he had a pleasant voice.

（7）弹唱人洋洋得意,陶醉在梦幻中。

Being immensely proud, he was intoxicated by his dream.

（8）他胸有成竹地
登台表演。

He had a well-
thought-out plan
to perform on the
stage.

（9）不料，一张口还
是那刺耳的嗓门。人
们厌恶地把他轰走
了。

Unexpectedly,
he still had a bad
voice. The audience
jeered at him hat-
edly.

小偷和公鸡

THE THIEF AND THE COCK

原著:〔古希腊〕伊索　　　Written by Aesop (Gr.)

改编:芊　里　　　　　　Adapted by Qian Li

翻译:王宁娜　　　　　　Translated by Wang Ningna

绘画:耿　默　　　　　　Illustrated by Geng Mo

（1）有家农户,养了一只公鸡。

Once a farmer raised a cock.

（2）公鸡忠于职守，深得主人喜爱。

The cock was devoted to his duty and was loved by his master.

（3）一天深夜，一个小偷溜进了农夫家中。

One night, a thief stole into the farmer's yard.

（4）他没找到别的，便把公鸡捉走了。

As he found nothing, he took the cock with him.

（5）小偷要杀掉公鸡做下酒菜。

The thief was going to kill the cock for his meal.

（6）公鸡请求说："我天不亮就唤醒主人，对人有益。放了我吧！"

The cock asked: "I crow and wake my master up at daybreak. I do good for people, please let me go!"

（7）小偷说："正因为你唤醒人们，我才偷不成东西！"

"I can't steal things just because you wake people up," replied the thief.

（8）小偷狠狠地拿起刀,朝公鸡刺去。

The thief took up the knife and stabbed at the cock fiercely.

（9）公鸡临死才明白,对好人有益的事对坏人却有害。

The thing that is good to good people is bad to a devil. The cock didn't realize the truth until his death.

狗和厨师

THE DOG AND THE COOK

原著:〔古希腊〕伊索

改编: 芊 里

翻译: 王宁娜

绘画: 卢洪刚

Written by Aesop (Gr.)

Adapted by Qian Li

Translated by Wang Ningna

Illustrated by Lu Honggang

（1）一条狗，平时装得很温顺，常在厨房前走动。

A dog, pretending to be very meek, often wandered in front of a kitchen.

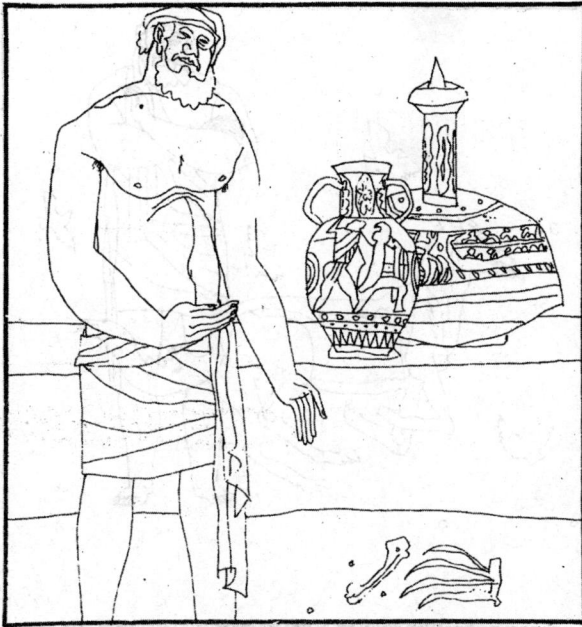

（2）厨师可怜它,经常扔些骨头给它吃。

A cook had pity on him, and sometimes gave him some bones to eat.

（3）狗故意装出一副感激不尽的样子。

The dog put on a grateful look intentionally.

（4）厨师把狗当成了好伙伴，亲热地嬉闹。

The cook took the dog as his good fellow and played with him intimately.

（5）狗可以自由地出入厨房，无人阻挡它。

Now, the dog could come in and go out of the kitchen freely. No one prevented him.

（6）狗见时机成熟，趁厨师不留神，偷吃了一条小鱼。

The dog thought that time was ripe for him. So he stole a small fish without the notice of the cook.

（7）不久，又偷吃了一块蛋糕。

Not long after that, he stole a cake.

（8）厨师发觉被盗，但没想到是狗干的。

The cook found something missing, but he didn't think that it was the dog who did it.

（9）主人气愤地训斥厨师,狗在旁边暗自得意。

The master blamed the cook for the theft while the dog was sitting by his side smiling secretly.

(10) 狗得寸进尺。一天，又偷了个猪心悄悄溜走了。

The dog became more and more greedy.One day,he stole a pig-heart.

(11) 厨师发觉丢了猪心，转身来找，发现了逃走的狗。

The cook found the pig-heart had missed. Turning around,he saw the dog running away with it.

（12）他骂道："畜
生，你虽然偷去一个
心，却也给了我一个
心。"

"You dirty
dog," he cursed,"you
stole a heart from
me;but you give me
a heart against you. "

（13）从此，他时时
提防。狗连骨头也吃
不到了。

From then on,
the dog got nothing
from him, for the
cook was always on
guard.

衔肉的狗

A DOG WITH A BIT OF MEAT

原著:〔古希腊〕伊索　　　　Written by Aesop (Gr.)

改编: 芊　里　　　　　　　Adapted by Qian Li

翻译: 王宁娜　　　　　　　Translated by Wang Ningna

绘画: 赵勤国　　　　　　　Illustrated by Zhao Qinguo

（1）一只狗从主人家偷了一块肉，逃了出来。

A dog stole a bit of meat from his master and ran away.

（2）它慌慌张张地跑到河边，来到小桥上。

He hurried to a river bank and went onto a bridge.

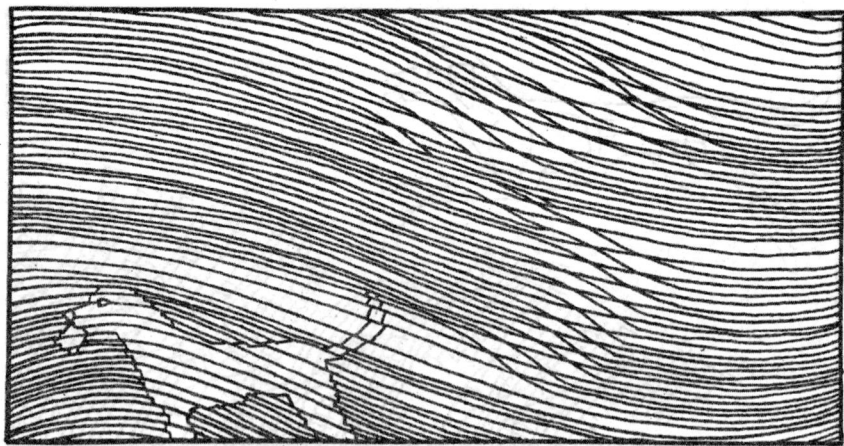

（3）忽然，它看见了自己在河水中的倒影。

Suddenly, he saw his own reflection in the water.

（4）———一条狗嘴里衔着一块肉，正怔怔地望着它。

Another dog, with a bit of meat between his teeth, was looking at him with terror.

（5）桥上的狗一动，河里的狗也一动。

The dog reflected in the water moved the moment the dog on the bridge moved.

（6）"好呀,想跑!"贪心的狗大叫一声朝河里扑去!

    "Ah, you want to run away!" Giving a loud bark, the greedy dog sprang at it.

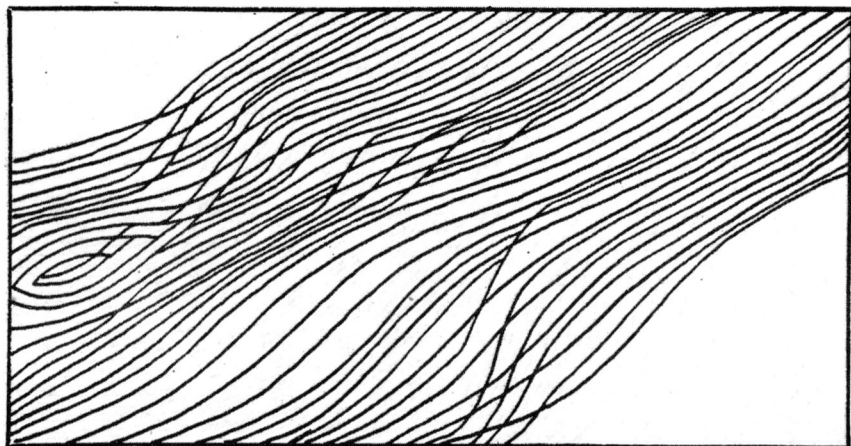

（7）"扑通!"狗栽进了河里,河里的狗不见了。

    Down fell the dog into the water, and the former dog in the water disappeared.

（8）狗险些淹死,好不容易才爬到岸上。

　　The dog was nearly drowned,he struggled hard and got onto the bank at last.

（9）结果,河里的肉没抢到,原有的肉也被河水冲走了。

　　As a result,the meat he had before was gone with the water and so was the reflected one.

上当的狼

THE DOG BEING CHEATED

原著：〔古希腊〕伊索
改编：芊　里
翻译：王宁娜
绘画：袁　晖

Written by Aesop（Gr.）
Adapted by Qian Li
Translated by Wang Ningna
Illustrated by Yuan Hui

（1）狗在畜圈前警卫，累了，不知不觉睡着了。

A dog was watching over the fold. Being rather tired, he fell fast asleep soon.

（2）狼悄悄来到畜圈前，突然袭击，狗被抓住了。狼得意地想饱餐一顿。

A wolf came to the fold quietly. All of a sudden, he caught the dog. Much pleased with himself, the wolf wanted to eat it as a nice meal.

（3）狗对狼说："我现在又瘦又小，请您稍等几天再吃，好吗？"

"Mr. Wolf," cried the dog, "I'm now all skin and bone, would you please wait and eat me a few days later?"

（4）"因为我的主人就要举行婚礼了,那时我吃得肥肥的,不更可口吗? "

"My master will hold a wedding party in a few days. It will be very delicious to eat me when I get fat. "

（5）狼信以为真,抹抹口水,把狗放走了。

The wolf took the dog's word for it. Wiping away the saliva which had drooled from his mouth, he let the dog go.

（6）过了几天，狼来了，发现狗睡在屋顶上。

A few days passed. The wolf came only to find that the dog was sleeping on the top of the roof.

（7）狼在下面叫狗："怎么，你忘了你许诺的话啦？"

"Why, don't you forget your promise?"the wolf shouted below.

（8）狗回答说："狼，你以后再抓住我，就不要再等婚礼了。"

"Mr. Wolf, don't wait for the wedding party and catch me next time!" answered the dog.

（9）狼这才发觉上了狗的当，只好悻悻地离去。

The wolf realized that he was cheated and went away angrily.

狮子和农夫

THE LION AND THE FARMER

原著：〔古希腊〕伊索　　　　　Written by Aesop（Gr.）

改编：芊　里　　　　　　　　　Adapted by Qian Li

翻译：王宁娜　　　　　　　　　Translated by Wang Ningna

绘画：潘东篱　　　　　　　　　Illustrated by Pan Dongli

（1）农夫有个女儿，美丽无比，百里挑一。

A farmer had a daughter, and everybody said that she was the most beautiful one among a hundred girls.

（2）狮子知道了，上门来求婚。农夫很不情愿，但又不敢拒绝。

On hearing the news, a lion came and made an offer of marriage. The farmer was unwilling to marry his daughter to the lion; but he couldn't turn down his request, for he was afraid of the lion.

（3）狮子再三催促："怎么样？快答应我吧！"

The lion pressured him again, "How about it? Agree with me!"

（4）农夫心生一计："大王作小女的新郎，十分相配，只是……"

An idea suddenly struck the farmer. He said:"My Lord, you match my little daughter very well, only……"

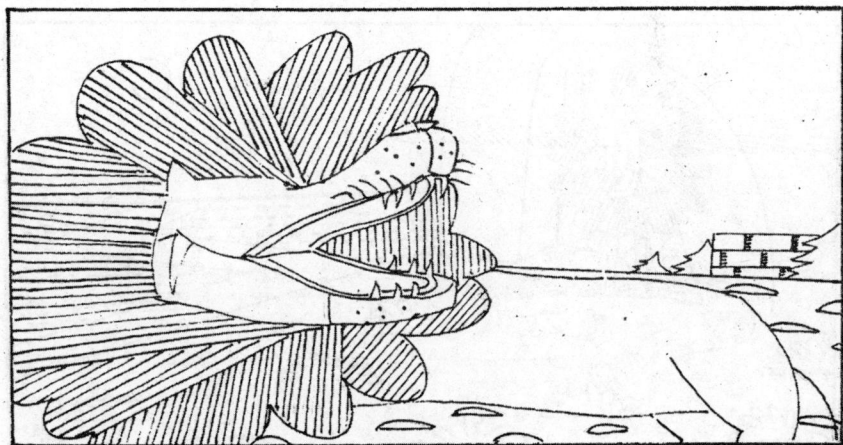

（5）"怎么啦？"狮子大吼一声，张牙舞爪。

"Only what?" the lion roared with fangs bared and claws sticking out.

（6）"只是，小女害怕大王的牙齿和利爪。请你把它除掉好吗？"

"Only my daughter was afraid of your teeth and claws. Would you get rid of them?"

（7）狮子回到山洞里，忍痛拔了牙齿，剁掉了爪子。

The lion returned to his cave. With great pain, he pulled all his teeth out and cut out all his claws.

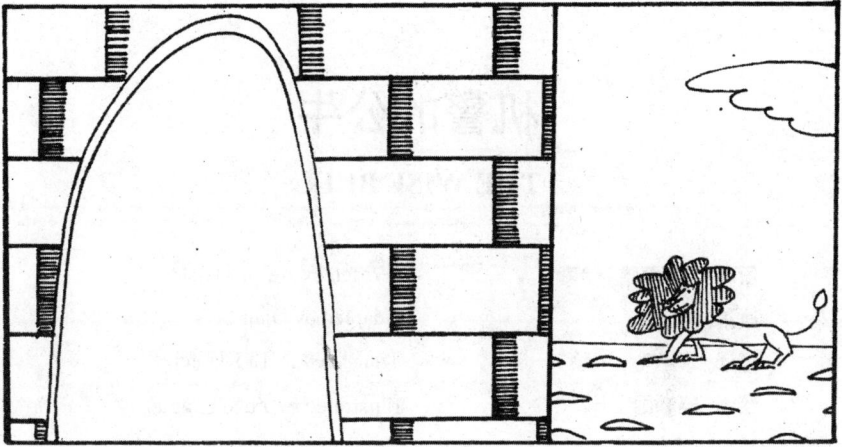

（8）狮子第二次登门求婚。

The lion came back and made an offer of marriage for the second time.

（9）农夫二话没说，用棍子把狮子打跑了。

Without saying a word, the farmer drove the lion away with a stick.

机警的公牛

THE WISE BULL

原著:〔古希腊〕伊索　　　　　Written by Aesop (Gr.)

改编. 芊　里　　　　　　　　　Adapted by Qian Li

翻译: 李小飞　　　　　　　　　Translated by Li Xiaofei

绘画: 赵勤国　　　　　　　　　Illustrated by Zhao Qinguo

（1）狮子打算吃掉一头大公牛。

A lion wanted to eat a big bull.

（2）可是，公牛在山坡上纵横驰骋，很难抓住它。

However, the bull, moving about freely and quickly, was difficult to catch.

（3）狮子终于想出一条诡计，将公牛骗到它的洞里。

The lion, at last, resorted to a trick. He invited the bull to his den.

（4）于是狮子对公牛说："我杀了一只绵羊，请你去会餐。"

So the lion said to the bull, "I have killed a sheep, so I invite you to dinner. "

（5）公牛答应了，随狮子朝山洞走去。

The bull agreed and followed the lion to the den.

（6）路上，狮子想：等公牛钻进山洞趴下时就将它吃掉。

On the way, the lion thought: when the bull declined to go into the den, I would eat him up.

（7）来到洞口，公牛没见到绵羊，却看见一口大锅。

On arriving at the entrance of the den, the bull saw no sign of any sheep, but a giant caldron.

（8）公牛急忙逃开了。狮子着急地喊："你为什么走了呢？"

The bull abruptly took his leave. The lion cried out anxiously, "Why do you go away?"

（9）公牛说："我发现你不像要吃羊，而是要吃牛。"

The bull said, "I see that you won't eat any sheep, but are likely to dine on a bull."

狮子和熊

THE LION AND THE BEAR

原著:〔古希腊〕伊索	Written by Aesop (Gr.)
改编:芊　里	Adapted by Qian Li
翻译:王宁娜	Translated by Wang Ningna
绘画:赵勤国	Illustrated by Zhao Qinguo

（1）狮子和熊一同去狩猎,大半天什么也没捉到。

A lion and a bear were hunting together for a whole morning, but got nothing.

（2）一只小鹿不小心落入了它们的圈套。

Unfortunately, a little deer fell into the trap they had set.

（3）狮子和熊一齐朝小鹿跑来。

The lion and the bear rushed at the poor deer.

（4）狮子说："这是我想出来的办法，鹿应归我。"

The lion said:"The trap was my idea. The deer should belong to me. "

（5）熊说："圈套是我爬树采来藤条做的，鹿该归我。"

"I've climbed the tree and collected the cane that made up the trap. It certainly belongs to me,"said the bear.

（6）它们争执不下，决斗起来。

They quarrelled and fought each other.

（7）狮子威武凶猛，熊力大无穷。打得难解难分。

The lion was mighty and violent, the bear strong and powerful. They locked together in the fight.

（8）狐狸见它们为争夺小鹿互不相让，暗自高兴。

A fox saw them fighting for the deer and smiled to himself.

（9）它们一直打了三天三夜，两败俱伤，瘫倒在地。

They had been fighting for three days and nights. Both were badly wounded. Not having any strength, they lay on the ground.

（10）狐狸旁若无人地跑来，把小鹿抢走了。

The fox came and took the deer away, as if no one was nearby.

（11）狮子和熊眼睁睁地看着到口的猎物被抢走，却站不起来。

The lion and the bear watched as their captive was taken away; but being helpless, they could do nothing.

狮子和老鼠

THE LION AND THE MOUSE

原著：〔古希腊〕伊索	Written by Aesop（Gr.）
改编：芊 里	Adapted by Qian Li
翻译：李小飞	Translated by Li Xiaofei
绘画：董小明	Illustrated by Dong Xiaoming

（1）森林中，一只狮子正在睡午觉。

In the forest, a lion was taking an afternoon nap.

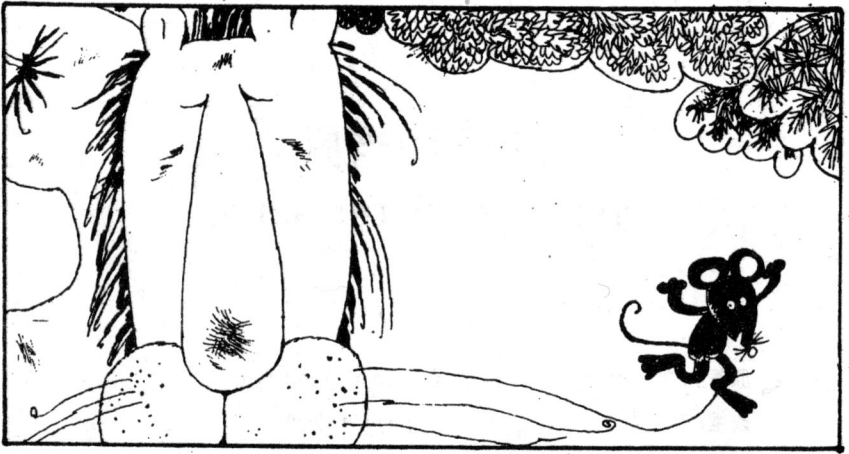

（2）一只老鼠出来找食物，不小心触着了狮子的胡须。

A mouse was out looking for food. Carelessly it touched the lion's whiskers.

（3）狮子被惊醒，一伸爪子把老鼠捉住了。

The lion was awakened and caught the mouse with his paw.

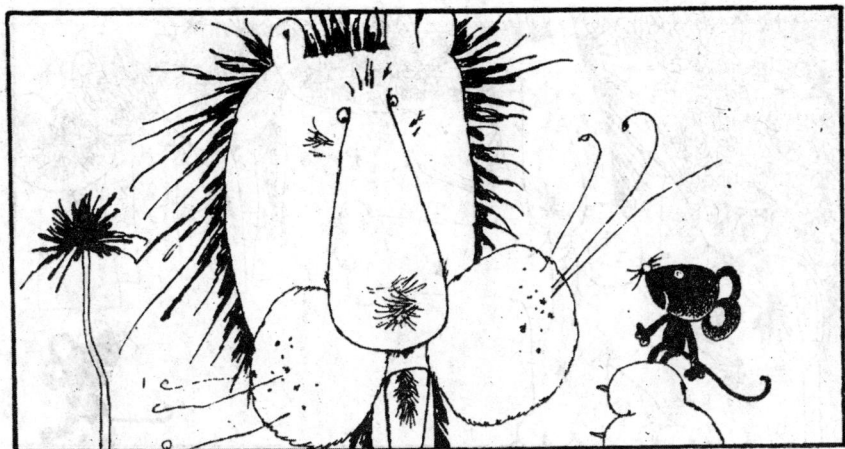

（4）"小东西,竟敢摸我的胡须,我吃了你!"

"You little thing, how dare you touch my whiskers? I'll eat you up."

（5）老鼠说:"大王息怒,请放了我,日后一定报答。"

The mouse said, "Don't be angry, King. Please spare my life. I will repay you later."

（6）狮子见它小得可怜，置之一笑，把老鼠放走了。

On seeing that he was so small, the lion laughed scornfully and let him go.

（7）不久，狮子不幸落入猎人的陷阱。

Not long afterwards, the lion happened to fall into some hunter's trap.

（8）猎人把狮子捉住，用绳子绑在树上，准备杀死它。

The hunter caught the lion, bound him with strong ropes and was about to kill him.

（9）狮子无可奈何地吼叫，可怎么也挣脱不开。

The lion roared helplessly but could not get free.

（10）老鼠听见了狮子的呼救声，便赶来用牙齿咬断绳子，狮子得救了。

The mouse, recognizing his roar for rescue. came up and gnawed the ropes with teeth. The lion was saved.

（11）狮子感谢老鼠，老鼠说："请记住，强者不可轻视弱者的力量。

The lion thanked the mouse. "Please remember this: the strong should not neglect the strength of the weak," said the mouse.

强盗和桑树

THE ROBBER AND THE MUL-
BERRY TREE

原著:〔古希腊〕伊索   Written by Aesop(Gr.)

改编: 芊 里   Adapted by Qian Li

翻译: 孙 健   Translated by Sun Jian

绘画: 王 恺   Illustrated by Wang Kai

（1）有个强盗，经常拦路抢劫，人们都憎恨他。

One robber often blocked the way in order to rob pedestrians. Everyone hated him.

（2）一天,这个强盗在路上杀了人,被别人碰见了。

　　One day, the robber killed a person, but was seen by others.

（3）人们呐喊着要抓住他,强盗落荒而逃。

　　All those people shouted to catch him, but he escaped.

（4）强盗跑到一棵桑树下，被迎面来的人拦住了。

Just as the robber reached a mulberry tree, he was stopped by a pedestrian coming from the opposite side.

（5）来人问他的两只手怎么是红的。

The pedestrian asked him why his hands were red.

（6）强盗说:"我刚
从桑树上下来,是吃
桑葚染红的。"

The robber
said:"I've just come
down from the mul-
berry tree. I ate some
mulberries and my
hands got red!"

（7）来人相信了强
盗的话,正要放他
走,追的人赶来了。

The pedestrian
believed him and let
him pass. Just then,
those people running
after the robber ar-
rived.

（8）强盗被团团围住，走投无路。

The robber was surrounded by them and had no way to escape.

（9）人们把强盗捉住，钉在了桑树上，要饿死他。

The robber was caught and was spiked onto the mulberry tree. Those people would make him starve to death.

（10）强盗苦苦哀求
桑树说："给我点桑
葚吃,救救我吧!"

The robber
begged the mulberry
tree sadly:"Please
give me some mul-
berries to eat. Help
me!"

（11）桑树说:"你杀
了人,却把罪恶栽到
我身上,我不会同情
你的。"

The mulberry
tree said:"It's you
who have killed the
man. But you passed
the accusation to me.
I will never have pity
on you."

狼和绵羊

THE WOLF AND THE SHEEP

原著:〔古希腊〕伊索　　　　Written by Aesop (Gr.)

改编: 芊　里　　　　　　　　Adapted by Qian Li

翻译: 李小飞　　　　　　　　Translated by Li Xiaofei

绘画: 梁平波　　　　　　　　Illustrated by Liang Pingbo

（1）一只狼吃饱了,在山坡上散步。

A wolf, who had just eaten his fill, took a walk on the hill.

（2）忽然，它发现一只倒在路旁的绵羊，便走了过去。

All of a sudden, he found a sheep which had fallen by the roadside, and came up to him.

（3）狼以为绵羊是吓倒的，不禁得意洋洋。

The wolf thought the sheep had fainted from fear and felt very proud.

（4）绵羊因腿扭伤而掉队，它以为这回大难临头了。

Having sprained his leg, the sheep had fallen behind. This time, he thought he was facing a disaster.

（5）不料狼说:"你只要讲三句真话，我就放了你。"

But the wolf said unexpectedly, "If you tell the truth three times, I'll set you free."

（6）绵羊已将生死置之度外,大声说:"一,我不愿碰见你。"

The sheep,having no regard for life and death,said loudly,"First,I am reluctant to see you."

（7）"二,如果命该如此,但愿碰见一只瞎眼狼。"

"Second,if I'm destined to meet a wolf,I wish I met a blind one."

（8）"第三，狼都不得好死。因为你们专门伤害懦弱者。"

"Finally, you wolves will die a notorious death, because you do harm especially to the weak."

（9）狼认为这几句话都是真话，就离开绵羊走了。

The wolf considered these were true and thus walked away.

（10）绵羊回到羊群中，讲了这事，伙伴们大吃一惊。

When the sheep was back to the flock and told the story, his companions were all shocked.

（11）绵羊说："看来说真话在敌人面前也是有力量的。"

Then the sheep said,"It seems that the truth carries much force even before an enemy. "

卖卜者

THE FORTUNE-TELLER

原著:〔古希腊〕伊索   Written by Aesop (Gr.)

改编: 郑黎明   Adapted by Zheng Liming

翻译: 孙 健   Translated by Sun Jian

绘画: 潘东篱   Illustrated by Pan Dongli

（1）一个卖卜算卦的人在市场上摆摊算命。

A fortune-teller set up a fortune-telling stall in a market.

（2）凭他一张巧嘴，
倒有不少人情愿出
钱请他预卜祸福。

　　Because of his
cunning words, many
people came to his
stall to pay him for
telling their fortune.

（3）正在他生意兴
隆的时候，他的邻居
急匆匆跑来了。

　　Just when he
had a good business,
his neighbour arrived
hurriedly.

（4）"你家的门被小偷撬开，东西全被偷走了。"邻居告诉他。

The neighbour told him:"The door of your home was pried open by thieves and everything was stolen."

（5）他听后大惊失色，于是便不顾一切地往家跑。

Hearing that, he looked frightened and then rushed home in a hurry.

（6）在场的人议论纷纷："连自己的事都不能预卜,怎能替别人算命? "

Everybody started to talk about what had happened: "How can he foretell the future for others? He can't do fortune-telling even for himself. "

（7）接着,找他算卦的人们一哄而散。

Then the people who waited expectantly for his fortune telling scattered immediately.

年轻的浪子和燕子

THE YOUNG LOAFER AND
THE SWALLOW

原著：〔古希腊〕伊索　　Written by Aesop (Gr.)

改编：郑黎明　　　　　　Adapted by Zheng Liming

翻译：孙　健　　　　　　Translated by Sun Jian

绘画：姜文浩　　　　　　Illustrated by Jiang Wenhao

（1）有个年轻的浪子，整天吃喝玩乐，把祖业挥霍一空。

There lived a young loafer who idled away his time in pleasure-seeking. He squandered all the family properties saved by his forbears.

（2）最后,他只剩下
身上的一件外衣还
值几个钱。

At last, he had
only one coat on his
body, which was
worth a little.

（3）一只提早飞来
的燕子落在他家房
檐上,可巧被他看
见。

One swallow,
which returned too
early from migra-
tion, landed on the
eaves of his house
and was found by
him.

（4）浪子以为夏天到了，天气不会冷了，就把外衣卖掉。

The loafer thought that summer was coming and there wouldn't be cold weather. So he sold his only coat.

（5）不想风暴又起，浪子没有外衣御寒，冻得直打哆嗦。

To his surprise, a windstorm came again. The loafer shivered with cold because he had nothing to keep out the cold.

（6）一同时，他看到
那只早来的燕子也
冻死在地上。

　　Meanwhile, he
saw that early com-
ing swallow already
froze to death on the
ground.

（7）浪子对燕子说：
"你的早来，毁了我，
也毁了你自己!"

　　The loafer said
to the dead swallow:
"Your early coming
destroyed both me
and yourself."

蝙蝠和黄鼠狼

THE BAT AND THE WEASEL

原著:〔古希腊〕伊索　　Written by Aesop (Gr.)

改编: 郑黎明　　Adapted by Zheng Liming

翻译: 孙　健　　Translated by Sun Jian

绘画: 蒲慧华　　Illustrated by Pu Huihua

（1）蝙蝠不慎跌在地上，被一只黄鼠狼捉住。

A bat carelessly fell down to the ground and was caught by a weasel.

（2）黄鼠狼要杀死蝙蝠,蝙蝠乞求饶命。

The weasel wanted to kill the bat. The bat begged for its life.

（3）黄鼠狼说:"我一生与鸟类为敌,你是鸟,岂能放过你?"

The weasel said:"Birds are always my enemies in my life, and you are a bird. How can I let you escape?"

（4）蝙蝠连忙辩解："我可不是鸟，我是鼠呀!"

The bat immediately explained:"But I'm not a bird. I'm a rat."

（5）蝙蝠长得的确像鼠，黄鼠狼便放了它。

The bat was really like a rat, so the weasel let it go away.

（6）后来,蝙蝠被另一只黄鼠狼捉住,也要杀它。

Later the bat was caught by another weasel who also wanted to kill it.

（7）蝙蝠流着眼泪,再一次乞求饶命。

The bat cried, begging for its life again.

（8）这只黄鼠狼说："我最恨鼠类，你是鼠，岂能放过你？"

That weasel said："I hate rats most. You're a rat, how can I let you escape?"

（9）蝙蝠辩解道："我可不是鼠，我是鸟呀！"

The bat explained："But I'm not a rat. I'm a bird."

（10）蝙蝠长得的确也像鸟，还会飞，这只黄鼠狼也相信了。

The bat is really like a bird and can fly. That weasel also believed in it.

（11）黄鼠狼爪子一松，蝙蝠又一次靠随机应变的本事保住了性命。

As soon as the weasel lifted its paws, the bat saved itself again with the help of its disguising strategies.

行人和阔叶树

PEDESTRIANS AND THE
BROADLEAF TREE

原著:〔古希腊〕伊索

改编: 郑黎明

翻译: 孙　健

绘画: 刘　威

Written by Aesop (Gr.)

Adapted by Zheng Liming

Translated by Sun Jian

Illustrated by Liu Wei

（1）盛夏的中午,骄阳似火。

At midsummer, the sun was scorching hot at midday.

（2）几个行人被晒得口干舌燥,躲到一棵阔叶树下乘凉。

Some pedestrians felt very thirsty because of the summer heat and hid themselves under a broadleaf tree to relax in the cool shade.

（3）这棵阔叶树根深叶茂,遮住了灼热的阳光。

The broadleaf tree had deep roots and luxuriant leaves. It shut out scorching sunlight.

（4）这几个人躺在树下，身上有了凉意，开始发起议论。

These people lay under the tree and felt cool. They started to talk.

（5）他们指手画脚地说，这棵树没有结果子，对人是无用的。

They made some indiscreet remarks that the tree had no fruits and was no use for people.

（6）阔叶树听着这几个人的评论，非常生气。

　　Hearing such remarks given by these people, the broadleaf tree got very angry.

（7）它说："我对人无用? 你们不是正在享受我的恩惠吗? "

　　It said:"I'm no use for people?But aren't you enjoying profit from me?"

行人和蝮蛇

THE PEDESTRIAN AND THE
PALLAS PIT VIPER

原著:〔古希腊〕伊索　　　　Written by Aesop (Gr.)

改编: 郑黎明　　　　　　　　Adapted by Zheng Liming

翻译: 孙　健　　　　　　　　Translated by Sun Jian

绘画: 孙爱国　　　　　　　　Illustrated by Sun Aiguo

（1）寒冷的冬天, 有个行人在路上看到一条冻僵的蝮蛇。

In a cold winter, a pedestrian saw a pallas pit viper frozen stiffly on the road.

（2）行人很可怜这条蛇，便把它揣进怀里，想把蛇温暖过来。

The pedestrian felt very sorry for that snake and placed it into his clothes close to his chest in order to warm it.

（3）渐渐苏醒过来的蝮蛇，却在那人胸口上咬了一口。

The snake gradually came to, but it bit the man in the chest.

（4）蛇毒非常厉害，受伤的行人必死无疑。

The poison was so violent that the pedestrian would certainly die.

（5）他临死时说："我是该死，谁让我救活蝮蛇这种坏东西!"

Before his death, he said:"I will die. Why did I save that bastard?"

驮神像的驴

THE DONKEY CARRYING A
GOD STATUE

原著:〔古希腊〕伊索　　　Written by Aesop (Gr.)

改编: 郑黎明　　　　　　Adapted by Zheng Liming

翻译: 韩明莲　　　　　　Translated by Han Minglian

绘画: 丛　林　　　　　　Illustrated by Cong Lin

（1）有个人赶着一头驮着神像的驴进城。

A man drove his donkey carring a God statue to the town.

（2）路上的人看到驴背上的神像，虔诚地顶礼膜拜。

Along the way, the passersby saw the God statue on the back of the donkey. They all paid homage to the God statue.

（3）驴以为大家是在拜它，十分得意，撒欢嘶叫，不肯前进。

The donkey thought these people were paying homage to itself. So it was very pleased with itself. It frisked and neighed and refused to go any further.

（4）赶驴人明白了是怎么回事,拿起棍子就打它。

The man came to realize what was happening; he picked up a stick and beat the donkey.

（5）赶驴人边打边骂:"蠢驴,人家是在拜神,轮到拜你的时候还早呢!"

While beating the donkey the man cursed:"You stupid donkey!People are paying homage to God. The day anyone pays homage to you is still far away."

野 驴

THE WILD ASS

原著:〔古希腊〕伊索　　　　Written by Aesop（Gr.）

改编: 郑黎明　　　　　　　Adapted by Zheng Liming

翻译: 韩明莲　　　　　　　Translated by Han Minglian

绘画: 刘祥成　　　　　　　Illustrated by Liu Xiangcheng

（1）身强力壮的家驴吃饱喝足了,躺在栏舍外晒太阳。

After much eating and drinking, a strong domestic donkey basked in the sun.

（2）野驴十分羡慕家驴的优越条件，便向家驴表示祝贺。

A wild ass envied the domestic donkey his favourable condition. So he came to congratulate the domestic donkey.

（3）后来，野驴发现，家驴每天要驮很沉重的东西。

Later, the wild ass found that every day the domestic donkey worked hard carrying very heavy things.

（4）赶驴人跟在后面不时地用棍子赶它、打它。

And the domestic donkey was driven and beaten now and then by his master.

（5）于是野驴又对家驴说："我不再羡慕你用吃苦换来的幸福了。"

So the wild ass spoke to the domestic donkey:"No longer can I envy your happiness which is gained by labour and hardship."

驴、狐狸和狮子

THE ASS, THE FOX AND
THE LION

原著：〔古希腊〕伊索　　　Written by Aesop (Gr.)
改编：郑黎明　　　　　　Adapted by Zheng Liming
翻译：韩明莲　　　　　　Translated by Han Minglian
绘画：孙爱国　　　　　　Illustrated by Sun Aiguo

（1）驴和狐狸合伙到森林里去打猎，它们说好要齐心协力。

The ass and the fox formed a party to go hunting in the forest. They agreed to make concerted efforts.

（2）谁知运气不佳，它们远远地看到了饥饿的狮子。

But to their bad fortune, they met a hungry lion who was seeking a meal in the distance.

（3）狐狸一看大难临头，便心生一计，抢先跑到狮子身边。

Realizing death was approaching, the fox quickly planned a scheme. He took the lead, running to the lion.

（4）狐狸对狮子说:"只要你不吃我,我可以把驴交给你。"

"So long as you don't eat me, I can offer you the ass," said the fox to the lion.

（5）狮子佯装答应,狐狸便跑回到驴的身边。

The lion pretended to agree, So the fox ran back to the ass.

（6）它巧施诡计,把驴骗进了一个陷阱。

The fox said honeyed words to the ass and easily tricked the ass, who fell into his trap.

（7）驴是逃不掉了,狮子一翻脸,先捉住了狐狸,把它吃掉了。

Obviously the ass was unable to escape. So the lion suddenly turned hostile. He caught the fox and ate it instead.

小偷和他的母亲

THE THIEF AND HIS MOTHER

原著:〔古希腊〕伊索	Written by Aesop (Gr.)
改编: 郑黎明	Adapted by Zheng Liming
翻译: 韩明莲	Translated by Han Minglian
绘画: 李承东	Illustrated by Li Chengdong

（1）从前,有个小孩从学校里偷了同学的写字板,回家交给母亲。

Many years ago, there was a schoolboy who stole a writing-board from one of his classmates and brought it home to his mother.

（2）母亲不但没有责
备儿子，反而称赞儿
子能干。

Instead of chas-
tising him, the moth-
er rather praised him
as a capable boy.

（3）后来，这孩子又
偷了一件衣服，母亲
更是对他大加赞赏。

Then this time
the boy stole a dress,
the mother praised
him much more high-
ly.

（4）孩子越长越大，偷东西的胆子也越来越大。

As the boy grew up, he became more and more bold with his stealing.

（5）东西越偷越大，越偷越多……

He began to steal things of greater and greater value. He stole more and more.

（6）有一次，儿子偷东西时终于被当场抓获。

Then one day he was caught in the act.

（7）由于罪行严重，他被判处死刑，五花大绑，推上刑场。

Since he was guilty, he was sentenced to death. He was tightly bound and led to the execution.

（8）刽子手们手中
刀光闪闪，小偷垂头
丧气。

The execution-
ers' knives were
flashing. The thief
was very dejected,
lowering his head.

（9）做母亲的，此时
只能捶胸痛哭。

At this moment,
the mother, beating
her breast and stamp-
ing her feet, cried out
in deep sorrow.

（10）小偷要求跟母亲贴耳说几句话，母亲走到儿子身边。

Before his death, the thief begged to be allowed to speak one word in his mother's ear. So the mother quickly drew near to her son.

（11）不料，小偷突然一口把母亲的耳朵给咬掉了。

Unexpectedly, the thief suddenly took a bite and bit off his mother's ear.

（12）母亲疼痛难忍，捂着伤口，大骂儿子不孝。

The mother was extremely pained. Yelling out, she covered her wound and cursed the unworthy son.

（13）小偷却说："如果我第一次偷盗时，你就管教我，能有今天吗？"

But the thief replied:"If you had subjected me to discipline the first time I stole things, how could I have come to this end today?"